Spider

Little Miss M

Graham Ralph & John Cary

BBC CHILDREN'S BOOKS

Little Miss M is sitting on a tuffet,

tucking into curds and whey.

Along comes Spider

and sits down beside her . . .

Until she frightens him away!

Little Miss M is hungry again

but things aren't what they seem . . .

and just as she sits down to eat . . .

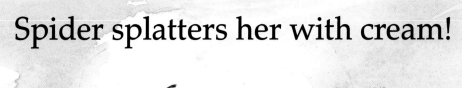
Spider splatters her with cream!

Her music is so loud

that Spider wants to shout.

Oh, Little Miss M,

you'd better watch out!

Little Miss M is eating once more,

but goodness! What a sight!

Spider starts to tidy up . . .

and gives Miss M a fright!

Little Miss M

is eating some sweets

but there's a surprise in store . . .

and as she runs away, they know

she won't be back for more!

Published by BBC Books,
a division of BBC Enterprises Limited,
Woodlands, 80 Wood Lane, London W12 0TT
First published 1993
Text and pictures copyright ©
Hibbert Ralph Entertainment Limited 1993
Based on the BBC television series
Words and Music: Richard Warner • Designs: Hugh Silvey and Wally Jex
Executive Producer: Iain Harvey
Produced by: John Cary • Directed by: Graham Ralph
ISBN 0 563 36797 0
Printed and bound in Great Britain
by Cambus Litho, East Kilbride